Katharina Graf
Höheweg 2
3303 Jegenstorf
031 96 05 82

**ROALD DAHL**

# THE WAY UP
# TO HEAVEN
## and other stories

The vocabulary is based on
Michael West: A General Service List of
English Words, revised & enlarged edition 1953
Pacemaker Core Vocabulary, 1975
Salling/Hvid: English-Danish Basic Dictionary, 1970
J. A. van Ek: The Threshold Level for Modern Language
Learning in Schools, 1976

Editor: Solveig Odland Portisch
Illustrations: Oskar Jørgensen

Printed in Denmark by
Grafisk Institut A/S, Copenhagen

## ROALD DAHL

was born on September 13, 1916 in South Wales of Norwegian parents. His father, who was a shipbroker, died four years later.

After he left school in 1932, he spent some months on an expedition exploring in Newfoundland. At eighteen he joined the Shell Oil Company in London. After training, the company sent him to Dar-es-Salaam, Tanganyika.

When the war broke out he drove 1,000 miles to Nairobi to volunteer for the RAF. He joined a fighter squadron in the Lybian desert where he was severely wounded. In 1942 he was sent to Washington as Assistant Air Attaché to the British Embassy.

There he began to write short stories. The first twelve, all about flying, were sold to major American magazines and were later published in a book "Over to You" in 1946.

He got himself removed from the Embassy into the more exciting field of Intelligence. He left the RAF at the end of the war with the rank of Wing Commander.

He married actress Patricia Neal in 1953. They have four children.

Roald Dahl has twice received the Edgar Allan Poe Award ("Edgar") of Mystery Writers in America.

Writings: "The Gremlins" (a juvenile) 1943; "Over to You" (story collection) 1946; "Sometime Never, a Fable for Supermen", 1948; "Someone Like You", 1953; "Kiss, Kiss" (story collection) 1960; "James and the Giant Peach" (children's book) 1964, filmed as "Willy Wonka and the Chocolate Factory"; "Switch Bitch" (story collection) 1974; "Danny and the Champion of the World" (children's book) 1976; "The Wonderful Story of Henry Sugar & Six More", 1977; "The Enormous Crocodile", 1978. He is also the author of the script "You Only Live Twice", a James Bond film. Roald Dahl owes part of his large American following to his CBS-TV series "Way Out".

# CONTENTS

Man from the South ............................ 6
Skin ................................................. 22
The Way up to Heaven ......................... 43
Mrs Bixby and the Colonel's Coat ............... 61

# Man from the South

It was almost six o'clock. I decided to buy myself a beer and go out and sit in a *deckchair* by the swimming pool and have a little evening sun.

I went to the bar and got the beer and carried it outside. Then I walked slowly down the garden towards the pool.

It was a fine garden with green grass and flowers and tall *coconut palms*. The wind was blowing strongly through the tops of the palm trees.

There were a lot of deckchairs standing around the pool. There were white tables and big *umbrellas* in bright colours. There were sunburned men and women sitting around in *bathing suits*. In the pool itself there were three or four girls and several boys all making a lot of noise and throwing a large ball to one another.

I stood and watched them. The girls were English girls from the hotel. I didn't know about the boys, but they sounded American. They were probably *naval cadets* from the U.S. *Navy* training ship which had arrived that morning.

I went over and sat down under a yellow umbrella where there were four empty seats. I settled back with my beer and a cigarette.

It was a pleasure to sit there in the sunshine and watch the young people *splashing* about in the green water.

---

*deckchair, umbrella, bathing suit,* see page 9
*naval,* of the *Navy,* a nation's warships
*naval cadet,* a young man, training to be officer in the Navy
*splash,* to make the water fly about

coconut palm

Just then I noticed a small, *oldish* man walking round the pool. He was dressed in a white suit and had white shoes on. He came quickly along the side of the pool, looking at the people in the chairs.

He stopped beside me and smiled. I smiled back.

'Excuse pleess,* but may I sit here?'

'Certainly,' I said. 'Do sit down.'

'A fine evening,' he said. 'They are all fine evenings here in Jamaica.' He sounded Spanish. I was sure that he was some sort of a South American. And old, too, when you saw him close. Probably around sixty-eight or seventy.

'Yes,' I said. 'It is wonderful here, isn't it.'

'And who, might I ask, are all these? They are not hotel people.' He was pointing at the pool.

---

*oldish,* old-looking
*) Excuse me, please

'I think they are American *sailors*,' I told him. 'They are Americans who are learning to be sailors.'

'Of course they are Americans. Who else in the world makes as much noise as that? You are not American, no?'

'No,' I said. 'I am not!'

Suddenly one of the cadets was standing in front of us all wet from the pool. He was about nineteen or twenty. He had red hair and was not very sunburned. One of the English girls was standing there with him.

'Are these chairs taken?' he said.

'No,' I answered.

'Do you mind if we sit down?'

'Please do.'

'Thanks.' he said. He had a *towel* rolled up in his hand. When he sat down he opened it and took aut *a pack of cigarettes* and a *lighter.* He offered the cigarettes to the girl and she refused; then he offered them to me and I took one. The little man said, 'Thank you, no, but I think I have a *cigar.*' He pulled out a silver case and took out a cigar. Then he produced a small knife and cut off the end of his cigar.

'Here, let me give you a light.' The American boy held up his lighter.

'That will not work in this wind.'

'Sure it'll work. It always works.'

The little man took the cigar away from his mouth, leaned forward and looked at the boy.

'All-ways?' he asked slowly.

'Sure, it never fails. Not with me anyway.'

The little man was still watching the boy. 'Well, well.

---

*sailor,* a seaman; a person who works on a ship
*lighter,* see page 12

umbrella

bathing suit    towel    deckchair

pack of
cigarettes    cigar

So you say this famous lighter never fails. Is that what
you say?'

'Sure,' the boy said. 'That's right.' He was holding the
lighter in his right hand, ready to light it. 'It never fails,'
he said, smiling now because he was on purpose *exaggerating* a little. 'I promise you it never fails.'

---

*exaggerate,* to make something seem better or worse than it is

'One moment, pleess.' The hand that held the cigar came up high. 'Now just a moment.' He had a strangely soft voice and he kept looking at the boy all the time.

'Shall we not perhaps *make a* little *bet* on that?' He smiled at the boy. 'Shall we not make a little bet on whether your lighter lights?'

'Sure, I'll bet,' the boy said. 'Why not?'

'You like to bet?'

'Sure, I'll always bet.'

The man looked at his cigar. I didn't much like the way he was acting. It seemed he was already trying to make something out of this, and to make the boy feel bad. At the same time I had the feeling that he was having a game of his own.

He looked up again at the boy and said slowly, 'I like to bet, too. Why don't we have a good bet on this thing? A good big bet.'

'Now wait a minute,' the boy said. 'I can't do that. But I'll bet you a quarter. I'll even bet you a dollar.'

The little man waved his hand again. 'Listen to me. Now we have some fun. We make a bet. Then we go up to my room here in the hotel where there is no wind. I bet you, you cannot light this famous lighter of yours ten times, one after another, without missing once.'

'I'll bet I can,' the boy said.

'All right. Good. We make a bet, yes?'

'Sure. I'll bet you a dollar.'

'No, no. I'll make you a very good bet. I am a rich man and I am a *sporting* man also. Listen to me. Outside the

---

*make a bet,* to take a chance of losing or winning money on the result of an event

*sporting,* ready to play a game, to take a chance

hotel is my car. It's a very fine car. American car from your country. Cadillac –'

'Hey, now. Wait a minute.' The boy leaned back in his deckchair and laughed. 'I can't put up that sort of property. This is *crazy*.'

'Not crazy at all. You strike this lighter ten times and it lights ten times and the Cadillac is yours. You would like to have this Cadillac, yes?'

'Sure I'd like to have a Cadillac.' The boy was still smiling.

'All right. Fine. We make a bet and I put up my Cadillac.'

'And what do I put up?'

The little man looked at his cigar which was still not lighted. 'I never ask you, my friend, to bet something you cannot *afford*. Do you understand?'

'Then what do I bet?'

'I make it very easy for you, yes?'

'Okay. You make it easy.'

'Some small thing you can afford to give away, and if you did happen to lose it, you would not feel too bad. Right?'

'Such as what?'

'Such as, perhaps, the little finger of your left hand.'

'My what?' The boy stopped smiling.

'Yes. Why not? You win, you take the car. You lose, I take the finger.'

'I don't get it. What do you mean, you "take the finger"?'

'I *chop* it off.'

---

*crazy,* mad
*afford,* to be able to pay for
*chop,* to cut off with a sudden blow

'Good God! That's a crazy bet. I think I'll just make it a dollar.'

The little man leaned back, spread out his hands and *shrugged his shoulders.* 'Well, well, well,' he said. 'I do not understand. You say it lights but you will not bet. Then we forget it, yes?'

The boy sat quite still, staring at the people in the pool. Then he remembered suddenly he hadn't lighted his cigarette. He put it between his lips, put both hands around the lighter and lit it. The *wick* burned with a small yellow *flame.* The way he held his hands the wind didn't get to it at all.

'Could I have a light, too?' I said.

'*Gee,* I'm sorry. I forgot you didn't have one.' – I held out my hand for the lighter, but he stood up and came over to do it for me.

'Thank you,' I said, and he returned to his seat.

'Are you having a good time?' I asked.

'Fine,' he answered. 'It's pretty nice here.'

There was a silence then. I could see that the little man had managed to trouble the boy with his *absurd* bet. The boy was sitting there very still. Then he started to move about in his seat and to *tap* both hands on his knees. Soon

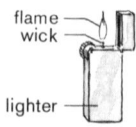

flame
wick

lighter

---

*shrug one's shoulders,* to draw up the shoulders to show that you are not interested, or don't know
*gee,* American word of surprise
*absurd,* silly; clearly wrong
*tap,* to knock lightly

he was tapping with one of his feet as well.

'Now just let me check up on this bet of yours,' he said at last. 'You say we go up to your room and if I make this lighter light ten times in a row, I win a Cadillac. If it misses just once then I lose the little finger of my left hand. Is that right?'

'Certainly. That is the bet. But I think you are afraid.'

'What do we do if I lose? Do I have to hold my finger out while you chop it off?'

'Oh, no! That would be no good. You might refuse to hold it out. This is what I will do: I will tie your hand to the table before we start and I will stand there with a knife ready to go chop the moment your lighter misses.'

'What year is your Cadillac?'

'Excuse me. I do not understand.'

'What year – how old is the Cadillac?'

'Ah! How old. Yes. It is last year. Quite new car. But I see you are not a betting man. Americans never are.'

The boy was quiet for a moment. Then he looked at the English girl, then at me. 'Yes,' he said quickly. 'I'll bet you.'

'Good!' The little man *clapped* his hands together quietly, once. 'Fine,' he said. 'We do it now. And you, sir,' he turned to me, 'would you be good enough to come along and be our *referee?*'

'Well,' I said. 'I think it's a crazy bet. I don't think I like it very much.'

'Nor do I,' said the English girl. It was the first time she had spoken. 'I think it's a very silly bet.'

---

*clap,* to strike together
*referee,* (in games) a judge

'Are you serious about cutting off this boy's finger if he loses?'

'Certainly I am. Also about giving him the Cadillac if he wins. Come now. We go to my room.'

He stood up. 'Would you like to put on some clothes first?' he said.

'No,' the boy answered. 'I'll come like this.' Then he turned to me. 'Please do me a favour and come along as a referee.'

'All right,' I said. 'I'll come along, but I don't like the bet.'

'You come too,' he said to the girl. 'You come and watch.'

The little man led the way back through the garden to the hotel. He was almost jumping as he walked along.

'Would you like to see the car first? It's just here,' he said.

He took us to where we could see the front driveway of the hotel. Then he stopped and pointed to a beautiful green Cadillac parked close by.

'Say, that's a nice car,' the boy said.

'All right. Now we go up and see if you can win it.'

We followed him up to the first floor of the building. He opened his door and we all entered a large *double bedroom*. There was a woman's dress lying across one of the beds.

'First,' he said, 'we have a little *martini*.'

The drinks were on a small table in the corner, and there was ice and several glasses. The little man rang the bell and began to make the martinis. Then there was a

---

*double bedroom,* a room with two beds
*martini,* a drink made with gin and dry vermouth

knock on the door and a *coloured maid* came in.

'Ah!' he said, and set down the bottle. 'Will you do something for me, pleess?' He gave the maid a pound note. 'You keep that,' he said. 'And now we are going to play a little game in here. I want you to go off and find three things for me. I want some *nails;* I want a *hammer,* and I want a chopping knife which you can find in the kitchen.'

'A chopping knife!' The maid opened her eyes wide and clapped her hands in front of her. 'You mean a real chopping knife?'

'Yes, yes, of course. Come on now, pleess. Surely you can find those things for me.'

'Yes, sir, I'll try to get them.' And off she went.

The little man handed round the martinis. We stood there and drank them slowly, the boy and the English girl in their bathing suits. She was watching him over the top of her glass all the time; the little man in his white suit was drinking his martini and looking at the girl.

I didn't know what to make of it all. The man seemed serious about the bet and he seemed serious about cutting off the finger. What if the boy lost? Then we would have to rush him to the hospital in the Cadillac that he hadn't won. That would be a fine thing. Now wouldn't that be a really fine thing. It would be a crazy and *unnecessary* thing so far as I could see.

*coloured,* belonging to a dark-skinned race
*maid,* a girl working in a hotel
*unnecessary,* not needed; not necessary

15

'Don't you think this is rather a silly bet?' I said.

'I think it's a fine bet,' the boy answered. He had already had one large martini.

'I think it is a very silly bet,' the girl said. 'What will happen if you lose?'

'It won't matter. Now that I think of it, I can't remember that I have ever had any use for the little finger on my left hand. Here he is.' The boy took hold of the finger. 'Here he is and he hasn't done a thing for me yet. So why shouldn't I bet him? I think it's a fine bet.'

The little man smiled and filled our glasses again.

'Before we begin,' he said, 'I will present to the referee the key of the car.' He produced a key from his pocket and gave it to me. 'The papers,' he said, 'the owning papers* are in the pocket of the car.'

Then the coloured maid came in again. In one hand she carried the knife and in the other a hammer and a bag of nails.

'Good! You got it all. Thank you, thank you. Now you can go.' He waited till the maid had closed the door, then he said. 'Now we prepare ourselves, yes?' And to the boy, 'Help me, pleess, with this table. We carry it out a little.'

It was the usual kind of hotel writing table. They carried it out into the room away from the wall and took away the writing things.

'And now,' he said, 'a chair.' He picked up a chair and placed it beside the table. He was working quickly, like a person preparing games at a children's party. 'And now the nails. I must put in the nails.' He fetched the nails and began to hammer them into the top of the table.

---

*) *ownership certificate,* papers showing who owns a car

We stood there, the boy, the girl, and I, with the martinis in our hands, and watched the little man at work. We watched him hammer two nails into the table. He allowed a small part of each one to stick up.

Anyone would think the *son of a bitch* had done this before, I told myself. Table, nails, hammer, chopping knife. He knows just what he needs and how to *arrange* it.

'And now,' he said, 'all we need is some *string*.' He found some string. 'All right, at last we are ready. Will you pleess sit here at the table?' he said to the boy.

The boy put his glass away and sat down.

'Now place the left hand between these two nails. The nails are only so I can tie your hand in place. All right, good. Now I tie your hand to the table – so.'

He made a good job of it. When he had finished, it was impossible for the boy to draw his hand away. But he could move his fingers.

»Now pleess, close your hand except your little finger. You must leave the little finger sticking out, lying on the table.'

'Very good! Very good! Now we are ready. You hold the lighter with your right hand. But one moment, pleess.'

He went over to the bed and picked up the chopping knife. He came back and stood beside the table with the knife in his hand.

'We are all ready?' he said. 'Mister referee, you must say when we shall begin.'

The English girl was standing there in her blue bath-

---

*son of a bitch,* (US) a bad name for a person you don't like
*arrange,* to prepare; to put in order
*string,* see page 15

ing suit right behind the boy's chair. She was just standing there, not saying anything. The boy was sitting quite still, holding the lighter in his right hand, looking at the chopping knife. The little man was looking at me.

'Are you ready?' I asked the boy.

'I'm ready.'

'And you?' to the little man.

'Quite ready,' he said and lifted the chopping knife up in the air and held it there about two feet above the boy's finger, ready to chop.

'All right,' I said. 'You may begin.'

The boy said, 'Will you please count *aloud* the number of times I light it.'

'Yes,' I said. 'I'll do that.'

With his *thumb* he raised the top of the lighter, and again with the thumb he *flicked* the wheel. The wick caught fire and burned with a small yellow flame.

'One!' I called.

He flicked the wheel very strongly and once more there was a small flame burning on the wick.

'Two!'

No one else said anything. The boy kept his eyes on the lighter. The little man held the chopping knife in the air. He too was watching the lighter.

'Three!'

'Four!'

'Five!'

'Six!'

'Seven!' It seemed to be one of those lighters that

---

*aloud,* in a voice which can be heard
*thumb,* the short, thick finger of the hand
*flick,* to hit or strike lightly with a quick movement

worked. I watched the thumb pressing the top down on the flame. Then the thumb raising the top once more. This was an all-thumb operation. The thumb did everything. The thumb flicked the wheel. The little flame appeared.

'Eight!' I said, and as I said it the door opened. We all turned to see a woman standing in the doorway. A small, blackhaired woman, rather old, who stood there for about two seconds.

Then she rushed forward, shouting, 'Carlos! Carlos!' She took the chopping knife out of his hand and threw it on the bed. Then she took hold of the little man and began to shake him *vigorously*. She was talking to him fast and loud all the time in some Spanish-sounding language.

She shook him so fast you couldn't see him any more. Then she shook him more slowly and the little man came into view again. She pulled him across the room and pushed him on to one of the beds.

'I am sorry,' the woman said. 'I'm terribly sorry that this should happen.' She spoke good English.

'It's too bad,' she went on. 'For ten minutes I leave him alone to go and have my hair washed and I come back and he is at it again.' She looked sorry and deeply concerned.

The boy was *untying* his hand from the table. The English girl and I stood there and said nothing.

'He is dangerous,' the woman said. 'Down where we live at home he has taken forty-seven fingers from different people. And he has lost eleven cars. In the end they

---

*vigorously,* with strength; strongly
*untie,* to set free

wanted to have him put away somewhere. That's why I brought him up here.'

'We were only having a little bet,' *mumbled* the little man from the bed.

'I suppose he bet you a car,' the woman said.

'Yes,' the boy answered. 'A Cadillac.'

'He has no car. It's mine. And what makes it worse,' she said, 'is that he should bet you when he has nothing to bet with. I am very sorry about it all.' She seemed a very nice woman.

'Well,' I said, 'then here is the key of your car.' I put it on the table.

'We were only having a little bet,' mumbled the little man.

'He hasn't anything left to bet with,' the woman said. 'He hasn't a thing in the world. Not a thing. As a matter of fact, I myself won it all from him a long while ago. It took time, and it was hard work, but I won it all in the end.'

She looked at the boy and smiled, a slow sad smile. Then she came over and put out a hand to take the key from the table.

I can see it now, that hand of hers; it had only one finger on it, and a thumb.

---

*mumble,* to speak with a low voice which is hard to hear

# Questions

1. What are people doing around the swimming pool?

2. Who are in the pool?

3. Describe the man from the south.

4. What does the young American do after he has joined the others at the table?

5. What kind of a bet does the old man suggest?

6. Why does the boy accept the bet?

7. How does the old man prepare the game?

8. In what way does the woman put an end to it?

9. What does she tell the party?

# Skin

That year – 1946 – the winter was very long. Although it was April, a cold wind blew through the streets of the city and snow clouds moved across the sky.

The old man who was called Drioli *shuffled* along the Rue de Rivoli\*. He was cold and *miserable*. He was all covered up in a dirty black coat; only his eyes and the top of his head could be seen.

He moved along looking without interest at the things in the shop windows – expensive shirts and ties, fine books. Then a *picture gallery*. He had always liked picture galleries. This one had a single painting in the window. He stopped to look at it. He turned to go on. He stopped again and looked back; and now, suddenly, he seemed to remember something, somewhere, that he had seen before. He looked again. It was a painting of some trees leaning to one side, blown by a strong wind. Below the picture, there was a little *plaque* which read: CHAÏM SOUTINE (1894-1943).

Drioli stared at the picture. Crazy painting, he thought. Very strange and crazy, but I like it . . . Chaïm Soutine . . . Soutine . . . 'By God!' he cried suddenly. 'My little *Kalmuck*, that's who it is! My little Kalmuck with a picture in the finest shop in Paris! Just *imagine* that!'

---

*shuffle,* to walk without lifting the feet from the ground
\*) street in Paris, France
*miserable,* very sad
*picture gallery,* room(s) for showing paintings
*plaque,* a flat piece of metal
*Kalmuck,* a member of a Mongolian race living in Russia
*imagine,* to form a picture in the mind; to think about

The old man pressed his face closer to the window. He could remember the boy, yes, quite clearly he could remember him. But when? It was so long ago. How long: twenty – no, more like thirty years, wasn't it? Wait a minute. Yes – it was the year before the war, the first war, 1913. That was it. And this Soutine, this *ugly* little Kalmuck, was then a *sullen* boy. He had liked him – almost loved him – for no reason at all, except that he could paint.

How he could paint! It was coming back more clearly now. Where was it the boy had lived? The Cité Falguière, that was it! He was pleased to have remembered the name. Then there was the *studio* with the single chair in it, the dirty bed; the parties with the cheap white wine, the fights. And always, always the angry, sullen face of the boy, working on a painting.

It was strange, Drioli thought, how easily it all came back to him now. There was the business about the *tattoo*, for example. Now, that was a mad thing if ever there was one. How had it started? Ah, yes, he had got rich one day, that was it, and he had bought lots of wine. He could see himself now as he entered the studio with the bottles under his arm. The boy was painting his (Drioli's) wife, who was standing in the centre of the room.

'Tonight we shall *celebrate*,' he said. 'We shall have a little party, us three.'

'What is it that we celebrate?' the boy asked, without looking up.

---

*ugly,* not pretty
*sullen,* quiet, not friendly
*studio,* the working-room of a painter
*tattoo,* see page 24
*celebrate,* to give a party in honour of someone or something

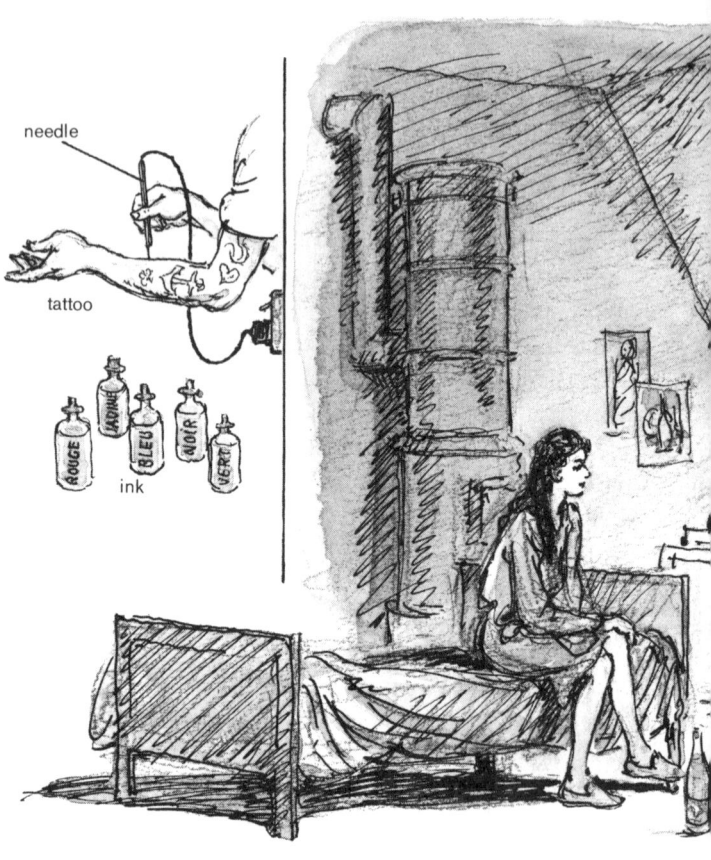

needle

tattoo

ROUGE JAUNE BLEU NOIR VERT

ink

'We celebrate,' Drioli said, 'because today I have made a lot of money with my work.'

'And I have made nothing. We can celebrate that also.'

'If you like.' Drioli was standing by the table with the bottles. He felt tired and wanted to get at the wine. Nine customers, all soldiers, in one day was all very nice. But the work was terrible for his eyes. He had never had as many as nine before. But it was evening now and he was

jacket

rich, and he had three bottles, one for his wife, one for his friend, and one for him.

The boy stopped working. 'Oh, Christ,' he said. 'How can one work with all this going on?'

The girl came across the room to look at the painting. Drioli came over also. He had a bottle in one hand and a glass in the other.

'No!' the boy shouted angrily. 'Please, no!' He took the

picture away and stood it against the wall. But Drioli had seen it.

'I like it.'

'It's terrible.'

'It's *marvellous*. Like all the others that you do, it's marvellous. I love them all.'

'The trouble is that I cannot eat them,' the boy said.

'But still they are marvellous.' Drioli handed him a glass of wine. 'Drink it,' he said. 'It will make you happy.'

Never, he thought, had he known a more *unhappy* person, or one with a *gloomier* face. He had first seen him in a *café* some seven months before, drinking alone. Because he had looked like a Russian or some sort of an Asiatic, Drioli had sat down at his table and talked.

'You are Russian?'

'Yes.'

'Where from?'

'Minsk.'

Drioli jumped up and kissed him, and told him that he, too, had been born in that city.

'It wasn't really Minsk,' the boy said. 'But quite near.'

'Where?'

'Smilovichi, about twelve miles away.'

'Smilovichi!' Drioli shouted. 'I walked there several times when I was a boy. You know, you don't look like a western Russian. You look like a Kalmuck.'

Now, standing in the studio, Drioli looked again at the boy as he was drinking the wine. Yes, he did have a face

---

*marvellous,* wonderful; very good
*unhappy,* sad
*gloomy,* dark; sad
*café,* a small restaurant or bar

like a Kalmuck – very *broad* with narrow eyes and black hair and the thick sullen mouth of a Kalmuck; but the hands – the hands were always a surprise, so small and white like a lady's.

'Give me some more,' the boy said. 'If we are going to celebrate then let us do it in the right way.'

Drioli gave him some more wine and sat down on a chair. The boy sat on the old bed with Drioli's wife. The three bottles were placed on the floor between them.

'Tonight we shall drink as much as we possibly can,' Drioli said. 'I am very rich. I think perhaps I should go out now and buy some more bottles. How many shall I get?'

'Six more,' the boy said. 'Two for each.'

'Good. I shall go now and fetch them.'

'And I will help you.'

In the nearest café Drioli bought six bottles of white wine, and they carried them back to the studio. They placed them on the floor in two rows and opened them, all six of them. Then they sat down again and continued to drink.

'It's only the very rich,' Drioli said, 'who can celebrate in this manner.'

'That is true,' the boy said. 'Isn't that true, Josie?'

'Of course.'

'How do you feel, Josie?'

'Fine.'

'Will you leave Drioli and marry me?'

'No.'

'Beautiful wine,' Drioli said. 'We are lucky that we are able to drink it.'

---

*broad,* wide

Slowly they began to get themselves *drunk*. They had done it before, but all the same there were certain rules that had to be observed. There were a great number of things that had to be said, then said again; and the wine must be *praised;* and it was important to drink slowly, so that there would be time to feel all the different stages of getting drunk. The best moment for Drioli was when he began to walk on air and his feet did not really belong to him. When he could look down at his feet and wonder what crazy person they belonged to and why they were lying around on the floor like that, in the distance.

After a while, he got up to turn on the light. He was surprised to see that the feet came with him when he did this, because he couldn't feel them touch the ground. Then he began to walk around the room and to look at the pictures that stood against the wall.

'Listen,' he said at length. 'I have an idea.' He came across and stood before the bed. 'Listen my little Kal-muck.'

'What?'

'I have a *tremendous* idea. Are you listening?'

'I'm listening to Josie.'

'Listen to me, please. You are my friend – my ugly little Kalmuck from Minsk – and to me you are such a great painter that I would like to have a picture . . .'

'Have them all. Take all you can find, but do not *inter-rupt* me when I am talking with your wife.'

'No. No. Now listen. I mean a picture that I can have

---

*drunk,* suffering from the effect of drinking to much wine
*praise,* to talk well of
*tremendous,* very good
*interrupt,* to stop a person while he is saying or doing something

with me always ... for ever ... wherever I go ... whatever happens ... but always with me ... a picture by you.' He reached forward and shook the boy's knee. 'Now listen to me, please.'

'Listen to him,' the girl said.

'It is this. I want you to paint a picture on my skin, on my back. Then I want you to tattoo over what you have painted so that it will be there always.'

'You have crazy ideas.'

'I will teach you how to use the tattoo. It is easy. A child could do it.'

'I am not a child.'

'Please . . .'

'You are quite mad. What is it you want?' The painter looked up into the dark, wine-bright eyes of the other man. 'What in heaven's name is it you want?'

'You could do it easily! You could! You could!'

'You mean with the tattoo?'

'Yes, with the tattoo! I will teach you in two minutes!'

'Impossible!'

'Are you saying I do not know what I am talking about?'

No, the boy could not possibly be saying that because if anyone knew about the tattoo it was he – Drioli.

'All I am saying,' the boy told him, 'is that you are drunk and this is a drunken idea.'

'You could make a picture of Josie. A picture of Josie upon my back. Why shouldn't I have a picture of my wife upon my back?'

'Of Josie?'

'Yes.' Drioli knew he only had to mention his wife and the boy would get interested.

'No,' the girl said.

'Darling Josie, please. Never in my life have I had such an idea before.'

'What idea?'

'That he should make a picture of you upon my back.'

'A picture of me?'

'*Nude*,' the boy said. 'That is a good idea.'

'Not nude,' the girl said.

'It is a tremendous idea,' Drioli said.

'It's a crazy idea,' the girl said.

'It is in any event an idea,' the boy said. 'It is an idea which should be celebrated.'

They emptied another bottle among them. Then the boy said, 'It is no good. I could not possibly manage the tattoo.'

'Then just the head,' Drioli said.

'I could not manage it.'

'It is very simple. I can teach you in two minutes. You will see. I shall go and fetch the *instruments*. The *needles* and the *inks*. I have inks of many different colours – as many different colours as you have paints, and far more beautiful . . .'

'It is impossible.'

'You will see,' Drioli said. 'I will go and fetch them.' He got up from his chair and walked, rather drunk, out of the room.

In half an hour Drioli was back. 'I have brought everything,' he cried, waving a brown bag. 'All you need is in this bag.'

He placed the bag on the table, opened it, and laid out

---

*nude,* with no clothes on
*instrument,* a thing used in doing something
*needle, ink,* see page 24

the electric needles and the small bottles of coloured inks. He threw off his *jacket*. 'Now look. Watch me and I will show you on my arm how easy it is. First, I choose my ink – let us use ordinary blue – and I *dip* the point of my needle in the ink . . . so . . . and I hold the needle up straight. Then I run it lightly over the surface of the skin . . . like this . . . and with the little motor the needle jumps up and down and *punctures* the skin and the ink goes in and there you are. See how easy it is . . .'

The boy was *intrigued*. 'Now let me practise a little – on your arm.'

He began to draw blue lines upon Drioli's arm. 'It is simple,' he said. 'It is like a drawing with a pen and ink. There is no difference except that it is slower.'

'There is nothing to it. Are you ready? Shall we begin?'

'At once.'

'Come on Josie!' cried Drioli. He was moving around the room arranging everything like a child preparing for some game. 'Where will you have her? Where shall she stand?'

'Let her be standing there, by the table. I will paint her with her hair down over her shoulders.'

'Tremendous!' Drioli pulled off his shirt and stepped out of his trousers.

'Sit on the chair,' the boy said. 'Sit back to front, then you can lean your drunken head against the back of it. Hurry now, for I am about to begin.'

'I am ready. I am waiting.'

---

*jacket,* see page 25
*dip,* to put into water, here into ink, for a short time
*puncture,* to make a small hole
*intrigued,* very interested

'First,' the boy said, 'I shall make an ordinary painting. Then, if it pleases me, I shall tattoo over it.' He began to paint upon the *naked* skin of the man's back. He worked quickly, applying the paint thinly so that it wouldn't get in the way afterwards when he was going to tattoo. All his attention was directed towards the painting. He didn't seem drunk anymore. In less than half an hour it was finished.

'All right. That's all,' he said to the girl, who immediately returned to the bed, lay down, and fell asleep.

Drioli watched the boy take up the needle and dip it in the ink; then he felt how the needle punctured his skin. It hurt but not too much, and it kept him from going to sleep. He watched the different colours of ink that the boy was using and tried to imagine what was going on behind him.

Far into the small hours of the morning the machine *buzzed* and the boy worked. Drioli could remember that when the painter finally stepped back and said, 'It is finished,' there was daylight outside and the sound of people in the street.

'I want to see it,' Drioli said. The boy held up a *mirror* and Drioli turned his head to look.

'Good God!' he cried. It was a *startling* sight. The whole of his back was shining bright with colour – gold and green and blue and black and red. The face itself was quite alive, the *background swirling* around her head in a mass of dark green waves.

---

*naked,* with no clothes on
*buzz,* to make a sound like that of a motor
*mirror,* a looking glass; a glass in which you can see yourself
*startling,* very surprising

'It's tremendous!'

'I rather like it myself.' The boy stood back and looked at it. 'You know,' he added, 'I think it's good enough for me to sign.' He took up the needle again and wrote his name with red ink.

The old man who was called Drioli was standing in front of the window of the picture-gallery in a sort of sleep-like state. It had been so long ago, all that – almost as though it had happened in another life.

And the boy? What had become of him? He could remember now that when he returned from the war – the first war – he had missed him.

'Where is my little Kalmuck?' he had asked Josie.

'He is gone,' she had answered. 'I do not know where, but I heard that a *dealer* had sent him away to Céret to make more paintings.'

'Perhaps he will return.'

'Perhaps he will. Who knows?'

That was the last time they had mentioned him. Soon afterwards they had moved to Le Havre where there were more sailors and business was better. Those were the good years, the years between the wars. They had a small shop and nice rooms and always enough work. Every day three, four, five sailors came and wanted pictures on their arms. Those were indeed the good days.

Then the second war had come. Josie was killed. The Germans had arrived, and that was the finish of his business. No one had wanted pictures on their arms any more

---

*background,* the space behind the figures in a picture
*swirl,* to move round and round
*dealer,* here a man who sells paintings

after that. And by that time he was too old for any other kind of work. He then made his way back to Paris. He hoped that things would be easier in the big city. But they were not.

Now, after the war was over, he had neither the means nor the strength to start up his small business again. It wasn't very easy for an old man to know what to do. He didn't like to *beg*. Yet how else could he keep alive?

He was still staring at the picture. So that was his little Kalmuck. Up to a few moments ago he had even forgotten that he had a tattoo on his back. It had been ages since he had thought about it. He put his face closer to the window and looked into the gallery. On the walls he could see many other pictures and all seemed to be the work of the same painter. A great number of people were walking around.

Suddenly Drioli turned, pushed open the door of the gallery, and went in.

It was a long room with a wine-coloured *carpet*. By God how beautiful and warm it was! There were all these people walking around looking at the pictures, well-dressed and serious with *catalogues* in their hands. Drioli stood just inside the door. He wondered whether he should go forward into this crowd. But before he had time to make up his mind, a voice beside him said, 'What is it you want?'

Drioli stood still.

'If you please,' the man was saying, 'leave my gallery.'

---

*beg,* here, to ask people to give you money
*catalogue,* a list of objects

'Am I not permitted to look at the pictures?'

'I have asked you to leave.'

Drioli didn't move. He felt suddenly terribly hurt and angry.

'Let us not have trouble,' the man was saying. 'Come

carpet

on now, this way.' He put a fat white hand on Drioli's arm and began to push him to the door.

That did it. 'Take your hands off me!' Drioli shouted. His voice rang clear down the long gallery. All the heads turned round as one; all the surprised faces stared down the length of the room at the person who made this noise.

Two men came running over to help. They tried to push Drioli through the door. The people stood still and watched. Their faces seemed to be saying, 'It's all right. There's no danger. They are taking care of it.'

'I, too!' Drioli was shouting. 'I, too, have a picture by this painter! He was my friend and I have a picture which he gave me!'

'He's mad.'

'Someone should call the police.'

With a quick movement of the body Drioli suddenly jumped clear of the two men. Before anyone could stop him he was running down the gallery, shouting, 'I'll show you! I'll show you! He threw off his coat, then his jacket and shirt, and he turned so that his naked back was towards the people.

'There!' he cried. 'You see? There it is!'

There was a sudden silence in the room. Everybody stood still. They were staring at the tattooed picture. It was still there, the colours as bright as ever. But the man's back was thinner now, and that gave the picture a strangely *wrinkled* appearance.

Somebody said, 'My God, but it is!'

The people crowde round the old man.

'It is fantastic, fantastic!'

'And look, it is signed!'

'Old man, when was this done?'

'In 1913,' Drioli said, without turning round.

'Who taught Soutine to tattoo?'

'I taught him.'

'And the woman?'

'She was my wife.'

---

*wrinkled,* with lines in the skin, produced by age

The gallery *owner* was pushing through the crowd towards Drioli. He was quiet now, very serious, making a smile with his mouth. 'Monsieur*,' he said, 'I will buy it.'

'How can you buy it?' Drioli asked softly.

'I will give you two hundred thousand francs for it.'

'Don't do it!' a voice said in the crowd. 'It is worth twenty times as much.'

Drioli opened his mouth to speak. No words came, so he shut it; then he opened it again and said slowly, 'But how can I sell it?' He lifted his hands, then let them drop to his sides. 'Monsieur, how can I possibly sell it?' he said in a very sad voice.

'Yes!' they were saying in the crowd. 'How can he sell it? It is part of himself!'

'Listen,' the dealer said, coming up close. 'I will help you. I will make you rich. Let us settle this matter together, just the two of us.'

Drioli watched him with fear in his eyes. 'But how can you buy it, Monsieur? What will you do with it when you have bought it? Where will you keep it? Where will you keep it tonight? And where tomorrow?'

'Ah, where will I keep it? Well, now ... It would seem,' he said, 'that if I take the picture, I take you also. The picture itself is of no value until you are dead. How old are you, my friend?'

'Sixty-one.'

'But you are perhaps not very strong?' The dealer looked Drioli up and down, slowly, like a farmer who sets a price on an old horse.

'I do not like this,' Drioli said, trying to get away. 'I

---

*owner,* one who owns
*) French word meaning Mr or Sir

really don't like it, Monsieur.' He went straight into the arms of a tall man who put out his hands and caught him gently by the shoulders. Drioli looked around. The man smiled down at him.

'Listen, my friend,' the man said, still smiling. 'Do you like to swim and lie in the sun?'

Drioli looked up at him, surprised.

'Do you like fine food and good wine?' The man was still smiling. He spoke in a soft manner. His hand was still resting on Drioli's shoulder. 'Do you like such things?'

'Well . . . yes,' Drioli answered, still not understanding what the man meant. 'Of course.'

'And the company of beautiful women?'

'Why not?'

'And lots of suits and shirts made for you? It would seem that you are in need of clothes.'

Drioli watched the man, waiting for the rest of his offer.

'Have you ever had shoes made for your own foot?'

'No.'

'Would you like that?'

'Well . . .'

'And a bell beside your bed to call the maid to bring your breakfast in the morning? Would you like these things, my friend?'

Drioli stood still and looked at him.

'You see, I am the owner of the Hotel Bristol in Cannes. I now invite you to come down there and live as my guest for the rest of your life. Your only duty – shall I call it pleasure – will be to spend your time on my beach in bathing costume, walking among my guests, swimming, drinking martinis. You would like that?'

There was no answer.

'Don't you see, all the guests will be able to look at this marvellous picture by Soutine. You will become famous, and men will say, "Look, there is the fellow with the ten million francs upon his back." Do you like this idea, Monsieur? Does it please you?'

Drioli looked up at the tall man. He was wondering whether it was a serious offer. 'It is a funny idea,' he said slowly. 'But do you really mean it?'

'Of course I mean it.'

'Wait,' the dealer said. 'See here, old man. Here is the answer to our problem. I will buy the picture, and I will arrange with a *surgeon* to *remove* the skin from your back. Then you will be able to go off on your own and enjoy the great sum of money I shall give you for it.'

'With no skin on my back?'

'No, no, please! You don't understand. This surgeon will put a new piece of skin in the place of the old one. It is simple.'

'Could he do that?'

'There is nothing to it.'

'Impossible!' said the tall man. 'He is too old for such an operation. It would kill him. It would kill you, my friend.'

'It would kill me?'

'Of course. Only the picture would come through.'

'In the name of God!' Drioli cried, struck with fear. He looked around at the faces of the people watching him. In the silence that followed, another man spoke quietly from the back of the group, 'Perhaps, if you offered this

---

*surgeon,* a doctor who operates
*remove,* to take away

man enough money, he might agree to kill himself. Who knows?' A few people laughed.

Then the tall man put his hand on Drioli's shoulder again. 'Come on,' the man was saying, smiling his broad white smile. 'You and I will go and have a good dinner and we can talk about it some more while we eat. How's that? Are you hungry?'

Drioli watched him. He didn't like the man's soft voice, nor the way he put his hand on his shoulder.

'*Roast duck* and Chambertin*,' the man was saying.

Drioli's lips became loose and wet.

'How do you like your duck?' the man went on. 'Do you like it very brown and *crisp* or shall it be . . .'

roast duck

---

*) French red wine
*crisp,* hard, but easily broken

'I'm coming,' Drioli said quickly. Already he had picked up his shirt and was pulling it over his head. 'Wait for me, Monsieur. I am coming.' And within a minute they had left the gallery.

It wasn't more than a few weeks later that a picture by Soutine, of a woman's head, painted in an *unusual* manner, turned up for sale in Buenos Aires. That – and the fact that there is no hotel in Cannes called the Bristol – causes one to wonder a little, and to pray for the old man's *health,* and to hope that wherever he may be at this moment, there is a beautiful maid that brings him his breakfast in bed in the mornings.

*unusual,* not usual
*health,* the state of one's body

# Questions

1. What is the condition of the old man?

2. What catches the old man's attention as he is walking down the street?

3. What did Drioli think of Soutine?

4. How did they meet?

5. How did they celebrate Drioli's success?

6. How did Drioli interest Soutine in the idea of a tattoo?

7. What happened to them after the first war?

8. How does Drioli come to be in the rich part of town?

9. What effect does it have on the people in the gallery when Drioli shows them the tattoo?

10. What does the artdealer suggest?

11. Why does Drioli decide to go with the "hotel owner"?

# The Way up to Heaven

All her life, Mrs Foster had had an almost *pathological* fear of missing a train, a plane, or a boat.

With Mrs Foster the simple worry about catching a train had become a serious *obsession*. At least half an hour before it was time to leave the house for the station, Mrs Foster would step out of the *lift*, all ready to go. She could not sit down or keep still. She walked from room to room until her husband, who must have noticed her state, finally came out of his *study*. He would then suggest in a dry voice that perhaps they had better get going now, had they not?

Mr Foster may have had the right to be *irritated* by his wife's silly way of acting. But that was no reason for making her feel even more miserable by keeping her

---

*pathological,* as of a sick person
*obsession,* a feeling or an idea which will not go away
*study,* here a room used for reading, working on business, etc.
*irritated,* rather angry

waiting unnecessarily. Of course, it is by no means certain that this is what he did. Yet whenever they were to go somewhere, he was just a minute or two late, and his manner was so gentle that he seemed to be playing some private game to make the poor lady suffer. And one thing he must have known – that she would never call out and tell him to hurry. He had trained her too well for that. He must also have known that if he waited one moment too long, he could *drive her* nearly *into hysterics.* On one or two special occasions it had seemed almost as though he had wanted to miss the train just to make the poor woman suffer.

If this were true, what made it worse was the fact that Mrs Foster was and always had been a good and loving wife, except for this absurd fear of hers. For over thirty years she had served him well. There was no doubt about this. So for years she had refused to believe that Mr Foster would ever want to make her suffer. But there had been times in the later years of their married life when she had begun to wonder.

Mr Eugene Foster was nearly seventy years old. He lived with his wife in a large *six-storey* house in New York City, on East Sixty-second Street, and they had four *servants.* It was a gloomy place, and few people came to visit them. But on this particular morning in January the house had come alive. The servants were hurrying about, making the house ready to be closed. The *butler* was bringing down the *suitcases* and putting them in the hall.

---

*drive her into hysterics,* make her lose control over herself, and perhaps begin to cry

*six-storey,* with six floors

*servant,* one who is paid to work for another, doing housework

*butler,* head servant

suitcase

Mrs Foster herself wore a *fur* coat and had a black hat on top of her head. She was flying from room to room to see that the servants did everything right. But she was thinking of nothing at all except that she was going to miss her plane if her husband didn't come out of his study soon and get ready.

---

*fur,* the skin of certain animals covered with fine hair

45

'What time is it, Walker?' she said to the butler as she passed him.

'It's ten minutes past nine, Madam.'

'And has the car come?'

'Yes, madam, it's waiting. I'm just going to put the suitcases in now.'

'It takes an hour to get to Idlewild*,' she said. 'My plane leaves at eleven. I have to be there half an hour before to check in. I shall be late, I just know I'm going to be late.'

'I think you have time enough, Madam,' the butler said kindly. I told Mr Foster that you must leave at nine fifteen. There are still another five minutes.'

'Yes, Walker, I know, I know. But get the suitcases in quickly, will you please?'

She began to walk up and down the hall. Whenever the butler came by, she asked him the time. This, she kept telling herself, was the one plane she must not miss. It had taken months to make her husband allow her to go. If she missed it he might easily decide that she shouldn't go after all. And the trouble was that he wanted to go to the airport to *see her off*.

'Dear God,' she said aloud, 'I'm going to miss it. I know, I know, I know I'm going to miss it.' Her eyes were very close to tears.

'What time is it, Walker?'

'It's eighteen minutes past, Madam.'

'Now I really will miss it!' she cried. 'Oh, I wish he would come!'

---

*) airport outside New York City
*see someone off,* to go with someone to the train, plane, etc. to say good-bye

This was an important journey for Mrs Foster. She was going all alone to Paris to visit her daughter, her only child. She was married to a Frenchman. Mrs Foster didn't care much for the Frenchman but she loved her daughter. And she wanted very much to see her three *grand-children*. She knew them only from the many photographs that she had received and put up all over the house. Each time a new picture arrived she would carry it away and sit with it for a long time. They were beautiful, these children. She stared at them with love and looked for signs in the small faces of that old *blood likeness* that meant so much. She had come more and more to feel that she did not wish to live out her days in a place where she could not be near these children. She wanted them to visit her, to take them for walks and buy them presents, and watch them grow. She knew, of course, that it was wrong to have thoughts like these while her husband was still alive. She knew also that he would never be willing to leave New York and live in Paris. It was a *miracle* that he had agreed to let her fly over there alone for six weeks to visit them. But, oh, how she wished she could live there always, and be close to them!

'Walker, what time is it?'

'Twenty-two minutes past, Madam.'

As he spoke, a door opened and Mr Foster came into the hall.

'Well,' he said, looking at his wife. 'I suppose perhaps we had better get going soon if you want to catch that plane.'

---

*grandchild,* the child of one's son or daughter
*blood likeness,* there is a blood likeness when members of the same family look like one another
*miracle,* a wonderful act beyond the power of man

'Yes, dear – yes! Everything is ready. The car's waiting.'

'That's good,' he said. With his head over to one side, he was watching her closely, and she was looking back at him – at this small, well-dressed man with a *beard* that covered most of his face. He had a special way of making small quick movements with his head. Because of this and because of the way he was holding his hands together high up in front of him, he was like a *squirrel* standing there – a quick *clever* old squirrel from the park.

'Here's Walker with your coat, dear. Put it on.'

'I'll be with you in a moment,' he said. 'I'm just going to wash my hands.'

She waited for him, and the tall butler stood beside her, holding the coat and the hat.

'Walker, will I miss it?'

'No, Madam,' the butler said. 'I think you'll make it all right.'

Then Mr Foster appeared again, and the butler helped him on with his coat. Mrs Foster hurried outside and got into the *hired* Cadillac. Her husband came after her, but he walked down the steps of the house slowly and stopped halfway to observe the sky.

'It looks a bit *foggy*,' he said as he sat down beside her in the car. 'And it's always worse out there at the airport.

 squirrel

 beard

---

*clever,* quick in learning and understanding
*hire,* to get the use of (something) by paying
*foggy,* filled with *fog,* see illustration page 50

The flight is probably *cancelled* already.'

'Don't say that, dear – please.'

They didn't speak again until the car had crossed over the river to Long Island.

'I arranged everything with the servants,' Mr Foster said. 'They are all going off today. I gave them half pay for six weeks and told Walker I would send him a telegram when we wanted them back.'

'Yes,' she said. 'He told me.'

'I'll move into the club tonight. It'll be a nice change to stay at the club.'

'Yes, dear. I'll write to you.'

'I'll call in at the house now and then to see that everything's all right and to pick up the *mail*.'

'But don't you think Walker should stay there all the time to look after things?' she asked gently.

'Of course not. It's quite unnecessary. And anyway, I would have to pay him for that.'

'Oh yes,' she said. 'Of course.'

'What's more, you never know what people get up to when they are left alone in a house,' Mr Foster said and with that he took out a cigar, cut off the end and lit it with a gold lighter.

'Will you write me?' she asked.

'I'll see,' he said. 'But I doubt it. You know I don't hold with letter-writing unless there's something important to say.'

'Yes, dear, I know. So don't you *bother*.'

They drove on, along Queens Boulevard, and as they

---

*cancel,* to stop something planned
*mail,* letters etc. carried by post
*bother,* to trouble oneself or others

fog

came nearer to the flat grass land on which Idlewild is built, the *fog* became thicker and the car had to slow down.

'Oh dear!' cried Mrs Foster. 'I'm sure I'm going to miss it now! What time is it?'

'Never mind,' the old man said. 'It doesn't matter anyway. It is cancelled now. They never fly in this sort of weather. I don't know why you bothered to come out.'

She couldn't be sure, but it seemed to her that there was suddenly a new note in his voice, and she turned to look at him. It was difficult to observe any change of *expression* under all that hair. The mouth was what counted. She wished, as she had often before, that she could see

*expression,* the look on one's face

the mouth clearly. The eyes never showed anything except when he was angry.

'Of course,' he went on, 'if by any chance it does go, then I agree with you – you'll be certain to miss it now. You might as well accept that. We can't drive fast in this fog.'

He didn't speak to her any more after that. The car went on very slowly. The driver had a yellow lamp that helped him see the road. Other lights, some white and some yellow, kept coming out of the fog towards them, and there was a very bright one that followed very close behind them all the time.

Suddenly the driver stopped the car.

'There!' Mr Foster cried. 'We're stuck. I knew it.'

'No sir,' the driver said, turning round. 'We made it. This is the airport.'

Without a word, Mrs Foster jumped out and hurried into the building. There was a mass of people inside, most of them unhappy passengers who were standing around the ticket *counters*. She pushed her way through and spoke to the *clerk*.

'Yes,' he answered. 'Your flight is *postponed*. But please don't go away. We are expecting this weather to clear any moment.'

She went back to her husband who was still sitting in the car and told him the news. 'But don't you wait, dear,' she said. 'There's no sense in that.'

'I won't,' he answered. 'So long as the driver can get me back. Can you get me back, driver?'

---

*counter,* table for serving customers in a shop, here where you show the tickets
*clerk,* one who works in an office, here behind the ticket counter
*postpone,* to put off till later

'I think so,' the man said.

'Are the suitcases out?'

'Yes, sir.'

'Good-bye, dear,' Mrs Foster said and leaned into the car and gave her husband a small kiss.

'Good-bye,' he answered. 'Have a good trip.'

The car drove off, and Mrs Foster was left alone.

The rest of the day was a sort of *nightmare* for her. She sat for hour after hour on a *bench*, as close to the counter as possible. Every thirty minutes or so she would get up and ask the clerk if the situation had changed. She always received the same reply – that she must continue to wait, because the fog might blow away at any moment. It wasn't until after six in the evening that the clerk told her that the flight had been postponed until eleven o'clock the next morning.

Mrs Foster didn't quite know what to do when she heard this news. She stayed sitting on her bench for at least another half-hour. She was wondering where she might go to spend the night. She hated to leave the air-port. She didn't wish to see her husband. She was afraid that in one way or another he would keep her from going to France. She would have liked to remain just where she was, sitting on the bench the whole night through. That

bench

---

*nightmare,* a bad dream

would be safest. But she was already terribly tired. It didn't take her long to realize that it was a silly thing for an old lady to do. So in the end she went to a phone and called the house.

Her husband, who was just about to leave for the club, answered it himself. She told him the news, and asked whether the servants were still there.

'They've all gone,' he said.

'In that case, dear, I'll just get myself a room somewhere for the night. And don't you bother yourself about it at all.'

'That would be *foolish*,' he said. 'You've got a large house here. Use it.'

'But, dear, it's empty.'

'Then I'll stay with you myself.'

'There's no food in the house. There's nothing.'

'Then eat before you come in. Don't be a fool, woman. Everything you do, you *make a fuss* about it.'

'Yes,' she said. 'I'm sorry. I'll get something to eat here, and then I'll come on in.'

Outside, the fog had cleared a little, but it was still a long, slow drive in the taxi. She didn't arrive back at the house on Sixty-second Street until late.

Her husband came out from his study when he heard her come in. 'Well,' he said, standing in the study door, 'how was Paris?'

'We leave at eleven in the morning,' she answered.

'You mean if the fog clears.'

'It's clearing now. There's a wind coming up.'

'You look tired,' he said.

---

*foolish,* silly
*make a fuss,* to worry over matters that are not important

'Yes,' she said. 'I'm very tired. I think I'll go to bed now.'

'I've ordered a car for the morning,' he said. 'Nine o'clock.'

'Oh, thank you, dear. And I certainly hope you're not going to bother to come all the way out again to see me off.'

'No,' he said slowly. 'I don't think I will. But there is no reason why you shouldn't drop me at the club on your way.'

She looked at him, and at that moment he seemed to be standing a long way off from her. He was suddenly so small and far away that she couldn't be sure what he was doing, or what he was thinking, or even what he was.

'The club is *downtown*,' she said. 'It isn't on the way to the airport.'

'You'll have time enough my dear. Don't you want to drop me at the club?'

'Oh, yes – of course.'

'That's good. Then I'll see you in the morning at nine.'

She went up to her bedroom on the second floor, and she was so tired from her day that she fell asleep soon after she lay down.

Next morning, Mrs Foster was up early, and by eight thirty she was downstairs and ready to leave.

*Shortly* after nine, her husband appeared. 'Did you make any coffee?' he asked.

'No, dear. I thought you'd get a nice breakfast at the club. The car is here. It's been waiting. I'm all ready to go.'

---

*downtown,* (US) in the main business district of a city
*shortly,* a short time

54

They were standing in the hall – they always seemed to be meeting in the hall.

'If you are going to take me to the club first,' he said, 'I suppose we had better get going soon, hadn't we?'

'Yes!' she cried. 'Oh, yes – please!'

'I'm just going to get a few cigars. I'll be right with you. You get in the car.'

She turned and went out to where the chauffeur was standing, and he opened the car door for her.

'What time is it?' she asked him.

'About nine fifteen.'

Mr Foster came out five minutes later. As on the day before, he stopped halfway down to look at the sky. The weather was still not quite clear, but the sun was coming through the *mist*.

'Perhaps you'll be lucky this time,' he said as he sat down beside her in the car.

'Hurry, please,' she said to the chauffeur. 'Please get going. I'm late.'

The man started the engine.

'Just a moment!' Mr Foster said suddenly. 'Hold it a moment, chauffeur, will you?'

'What is it, dear?' she saw him *searching* the pockets of his overcoat.

'I had a little present I wanted you to take to Ellen,' he said. 'Now, where on earth is it? I'm sure I had it in my hand as I came down.'

'I never saw you carrying anything. What sort of present?'

---

*mist,* a thin fog
*search,* to look or feel or go over (a place, a person) to try to find something

'A little box in white paper. I forgot to give it to you yesterday. I don't want to forget it today.'

'A little box!' Mrs Foster cried. 'I never saw any little box.' She began looking for it in the back of the car.

Her husband continued to look for it in the pockets of his coat, then he felt around in his jacket. 'I must have left it in the bedroom. I won't be a moment.'

'Oh, p l e a s e!' she cried. 'We haven't got time! Please leave it! You can mail it.'

'Stay here!' he commanded. 'I'm going to get it.'

'Be quick, dear! Oh, please be quick!'

She sat still, waiting and waiting.

'Chauffeur, what time is it?'

The man looked at his watch. 'I make it nearly nine thirty.'

'Can we get to the airport in an hour?'

'Just about.'

At this point, Mrs Foster suddenly saw a corner of something white pressed down at the back of the seat where her husband had been sitting. She reached over and pulled out a small white box. At the same time she noticed that it was pressed down deep, as though with the help of a pushing hand.

'Here it is!' she cried. 'I've found it! Oh dear, and now he'll be up there for ever looking for it! Chauffeur, quickly – run in and call him down, will you please?'

The chauffeur didn't care very much for any of this, but he climbed out of the car and went up the steps to the front door of the house. Then he turned and came back. 'Door's *locked*,' he said. 'You got a key?'

'Yes, wait a minute.' She began looking like mad in her

---

*lock*, to close a door so that it can only be opened with a key

handbag. 'Here it is! No – I'll go myself. It'll be quicker. I know where he'll be.'

She hurried out of the car and up the steps to the front door, holding the key in one hand. She put the key into the keyhole and was just about to turn it – and then she stopped. Her head came up, and she stood there without moving. Her whole body had stopped right in the middle of all this hurry to turn the key and get into the house. She waited – five, six, seven, eight, nine, ten seconds, she waited. The way she was standing still, with her head in the air, she seemed to be listening for some sound that had stopped and that she had heard a moment before from deep inside the house.

Yes, she was listening. She moved one of her ears closer to the door. Now it was right up against the door. She remained in that position, head up, ear to the door, hand on key, for still another few seconds.

Then, at once, she sprang to life again. She pulled the key out of the door and came running back down the steps.

'It's too late!' she cried to the chauffeur. 'I can't wait for him, I simply can't. I'll miss the plane. Hurry now, driver, hurry! To the airport!'

Her face had turned white, the whole expression of her face had changed. There was no longer that soft and silly look. Her face looked hard with a thin mouth and bright eyes. And her voice, when she spoke, carried a new note of strength.

'Hurry, driver, hurry!'

'Isn't your husband travelling with you?' the man asked, surprised.

'Certainly not! I was only going to drop him at the club. It won't matter. He'll understand. He'll get a taxi.

Don't sit there talking, man. G e t g o i n g! I've got a plane to catch for Paris!'

With Mrs Foster *urging* him from the back seat, the man drove fast all the way, and Mrs Foster caught her plane. Soon she was high up over the Atlantic. She settled back in her seat and listened to the sound of the engines. She was on her way to Paris at last. The new *mood* was still with her. She felt strong and in a strange sort of way, wonderful. She was so surprised at what she had done that her heart was beating fast. But as the plane flew *farther* and farther away from New York and East Sixty-second Street, a great sense of peace began to settle upon her. By the time she reached Paris, she was as strong and *calm* as she could wish.

She met her grandchildren, and they were even more beautiful than on the photographs. Every day she took them for walks, and bought them cakes and presents, and told them stories.

Once a week, on Tuesdays, she wrote a nice long letter to her husband, which always ended with the words »Now be sure to take all your meals every day. I'm afraid you may not be doing so when I'm not with you.«

When her six weeks were up, everybody was sad that she had to return to America, to her husband. Everybody, that is, except her. She did not seem to mind as much as one might have expected. When she kissed them all good-bye, there was something in her manner and in the things she said that made them feel that she might return in the near future.

---

*urge,* to try hard to get someone to do something
*mood,* the state of a person's feelings
*farther,* to a greater distance
*calm,* quiet; not worried

So six weeks after she had arrived, she sent a telegram to her husband and caught the plane back to New York.

When Mrs Foster arrived at Idlewild she was interested to observe that there was no car to meet her. She took a taxi into town. New York was colder than Paris, and there was dirty snow lying in the streets. The taxi drew up before the house on Sixty-second Street. The driver carried her two large suitcases to the top of the steps. Then she paid him off and rang the bell. She waited, but there was no answer. Just to make sure, she rang again. But still no one came.

So she took her own key and opened the door herself.

The first thing she saw as she entered was a lot of mail lying on the floor where it had fallen after it had been pushed through the letter box. The place was dark and cold. There was a strange *smell* in the air that she had never come across before.

She walked quickly across the hall and round the corner to the left, at the back. She had the air of a woman who knows what she is looking for. And when she returned a few seconds later, there was a contented look on her face.

She stopped in the centre of the hall, as if she didn't know what to do next. Then, suddenly, she turned and went across into her husband's study. On the desk she found his address book. Then she picked up the phone.

'Hello,' she said. 'Listen, this is Nine East Sixty-second Street . . . Yes, that's right. Could you send someone round as soon as possible, do you think? Yes, it seems to be stuck between the second and third floors. At least,

---

*smell,* that which you sense through the nose

that's where the *indicator* is pointing. Right away? Oh, that's very kind of you. You see, my legs aren't any good for walking up a lot of stairs. Thank you so much. Goodbye.'

Then she settled back calmly in the chair at her husband's desk and waited for the man to come and *repair* the lift.

## Questions

1. In what way did Mr Foster make his wife suffer?

2. Why was the journey specially important to Mrs Foster?

3. Why was Mr Foster going to stay at the club while his wife was away?

4. What difficulties did Mrs Foster meet with on her first trip to the airport?

5. What trick did Mr Foster use on the second day to try to make her late?

6. How did it happen that Mrs Foster decided not to wait for him?

7. In what way did Mrs Foster change after she left her husband?

8. What did Mrs Foster find on her return?

---

*indicator,* see page 43
*repair,* to make (something) work again

# Mrs Bixby and the Colonel's Coat

America is the land of *opportunities* for women. Already they own about eighty-five per cent of the wealth of the nation. Soon they will have it all. For women *divorce* pays well. It is simple to arrange and easy to forget. They can repeat it as often as they like and become rich that way. Or they can gain by the husband's death. The poor fellow usually dies from overwork.

Young men can see this happening all the time but they are still not put off. By the time they are thirty-six years old many of them have at least two ex-wives on the *payroll.* To support these ladies, the men must work like *slaves,* which is of course just what they are. As old age comes on too soon and they begin to realize their state, fear slowly enters their hearts. In the evenings they meet in little groups, in clubs and bars, and drink their whiskies and tell each other stories to keep up their spirits.

In these stories there are always three main characters – the husband, the wife, and the *dirty dog.* The husband is a good, hard-working man. The wife is false and cannot be trusted. She is always at some game with the dirty dog. The husband is too good a man even to think ill of her. Things look black for the husband. Will the poor man ever find out? No he won't. But wait! Suddenly the

---

*opportunity,* a (good) chance
*divorce,* the ending of a marriage
*payroll,* a list of persons receiving pay
*slave,* one who is forced to work for a master
*dirty dog,* here a man who has many love-affairs

husband *turns the tables* on his *deceitful* wife, and she is completely beaten.

There are many of these stories going around but most of them are too foolish to be worth repeating. One, however, is better than the others; and it happens to be true. It is very popular with men who have been caught out two or three times. If you are one of these miserable men, and if you haven't heard it before, you may enjoy the way it turns out. The story is called "Mrs Bixby and the Colonel's Coat", and it goes something like this:

Mr and Mrs Bixby lived in a small *apartment* somewhere in New York City. Mr Bixby was a *dentist* with an average *income*. Mrs Bixby was a *vigorous* woman. Once a month, always on Friday afternoons, Mrs Bixby would go by train to Baltimore to visit her old aunt. She would spend the night with the aunt and return to New York on the following day in time to cook *supper* for her husband. Mr Bixby accepted this. He knew that aunt Maude lived in Baltimore, and that his wife was very fond of the old lady. There was no reason why they should not have the pleasure of meeting once a month.

'Just so long as you don't ever expect me to come with you,' Mr Bixby said in the beginning.

'Of course not, darling,' Mrs Bixby had answered. 'After all, she is not your aunt. She's mine.'

So far so good.

---

*turn the tables,* to pass from a losing to a winning position
*deceitful,* false; not true
*apartment,* (US) flat
*dentist,* a person who looks after teeth
*income,* that which a person earns
*virgorous,* full of life and strength
*supper,* the last meal of the day

As it turned out, however, the aunt was not the only reason for Mrs Bixby to visit Baltimore. The dirty dog was a rich gentleman known as the *Colonel*. He lived in a lovely house just outside the town. He had no wife or family, only a few servants and several horses. Mrs Bixby spent most of her time in Baltimore in his company.

Year after year this affair between Mrs Bixby and the Colonel continued. After all, they met only twelve times a year so there was little or no chance that they should get tired of one another.

Eight years went by.

It was just before Christmas. Mrs Bixby was standing on the station in Baltimore. She was waiting for the train to take her back to New York. This particular visit which had just ended had been very *pleasant,* and she was in a good mood. But then the Colonel's company always did that to her. The man had a way of making her feel that she was a marvellous woman, someone very special; and what a very different thing that was from the dentist husband at home. He never succeeded in making her feel that she was anything but a *patient* in his waiting-room.

'The Colonel asked me to give you this,' a voice beside her said. She turned and saw Wilkins, the Colonel's servant. He was pushing a large, flat box into her arms.

'My heavens, what a large box! What is it, Wilkins? Was there a *message?* Did he send me a message?'

'No message,' the servant said, and he walked away.

As soon as she was on the train, Mrs Bixby carried the

---

*colonel,* an army officer
*pleasant,* that gives pleasure
*patient,* one under the care of a doctor, a dentist, etc.
*message,* a piece of news sent from one person to another

box into the Ladies' Room and locked the door. How wonderful! A Christmas present from the Colonel. She started to untie the string. 'I'll bet it is a dress,' she said aloud. 'It might even be two dresses. Or it might be a whole lot of beautiful underclothes. I won't look. I'll just feel around and try to guess the colour as well, and what it looks like. Also how much it cost.'

She shut her eyes and slowly lifted off the *lid*. Then she put one hand down into the box. There was some *tissue paper* on the top. There was also a card. She didn't pay any attention to it but went searching under the tissue paper with her fingers.

'My God,' she cried suddenly. 'It can't be true!'

She opened her eyes wide and stared at the coat. Then she *grabbed* it and lifted it out of the box. When she held it up and saw it hanging to its full length, it was so beautiful that she couldn't take her eyes off it.

Never had she seen *mink* like this before. The fur was almost pure black. At first she thought it w a s black; but when she held it closer to the window she saw that there was a touch of blue in it as well, a deep rich blue. Quickly she looked at the *label*. It said simply, WILD LABRA- DOR MINK. There was nothing else, no sign of where it had been bought or anything. But what in the world could it have cost? Four, five, six thousand dollars? Possibly more.

She just couldn't take her eyes off it. Nor, for that mat- ter could she wait to try it on. Quickly she took off her own plain red coat. Her heart was beating strongly, she

mink

---

*lid,* the cover for a box
*tissue paper,* thin soft paper
*grab,* to take suddenly
*label,* a small written note fixed on to something (to tell its con- tents)

couldn't help it, and her eyes were opened very wide. But oh God, the feel of that fur!

The great black coat came on almost like a second skin. Oh boy! It was the strangest feeling. She looked into the mirror. It was fantastic. Her whole *personality* had suddenly changed completely. She looked *radiant,* rich, marvellous, all at the same time. And the sense of power that it gave her! In this coat she could walk into any place she wanted and be treated like a queen. The whole thing was just too wonderful for words!

Mrs Bixby picked up the card that was still lying in the box. It was from the Colonel:

»I once heard you saying that you liked mink so I got you this. Please accept it with my *sincere* good wishes as a *parting gift.* For my own personal reasons I shall not be able to see you anymore. Good-bye and good luck.«

Well!

Imagine that!

Right out of the blue, just when she was feeling so happy.

No more Colonel.

What a terrible shock.

She would miss him very much.

She put the card away, but she noticed that there was something written on the other side:

»P.S. Just tell them that nice aunt gave it to you for Christmas.«

The smile immediately left Mrs Bixby's face.

---

*personality,* one's personal qualities of mind and character
*radiant,* shining
*sincere,* true
*parting gift,* a gift to or from someone who is going away

'The man must be mad!' she cried. 'Aunt Maude doesn't have that sort of money. She couldn't possibly give me this.'

But if Aunt Maude hadn't given it to her, then who had?

She had been so busy opening the box and trying the coat on that she hadn't thought about this important point.

In a couple of hours she would be in New York. Ten minutes after that she would be home, and her husband would be there to receive her. Even a man like Cyril, who always had his attention fixed on his dentist work, would start asking a few questions if his wife suddenly returned from a week-end with a six-thousand-dollar mink coat.

You know what I think, she told herself. I think the Colonel has done this on purpose to make me suffer. He knew very well Aunt Maude didn't have enough money to buy this. He knew I wouldn't be able to keep it.

But the thought of *parting with* it now was more than Mrs Bixby could bear.

'I've got to have this coat!' she said aloud. 'I've got to have this coat! I've got to have this coat!'

Very well, my dear. You shall have the coat. Now sit still and keep calm and start thinking. You are a clever girl, aren't you? You have fooled him before. So just sit still and think. There's lots of time.

Two and a half hours later, Mrs Bixby stepped off the train at Pennsylvania Station. She was wearing her old coat again and carrying the box in her arms. She got into a taxi.

---

*part with,* to give up

'Driver,' she said, 'would you know of a *pawnbroker* that's still open around here?'

'Lots along Sixth Avenue,' he answered.

'Stop at the first one you see, then, will you please?'

Soon the taxi pulled up outside a pawnbroker's shop.

'Wait for me, please,' Mrs Bixby said to the driver and entered the shop.

There was a big cat lying on the counter. The animal looked up at Mrs Bixby with bright yellow eyes. Mrs Bixby stood by the counter, as far away from the cat as possible, waiting for someone to come. She was staring at the watches, the rings, the eye-glasses, the false teeth. Why did they always *pawn* their teeth, she wondered.

'Yes?' the pawnbroker said, coming out from a dark place in the back of the shop. He went up to the cat and started *stroking* it.

'Oh, good evening,' Mrs Bixby said. She began to un-tie the string around the box. 'Isn't it silly of me? I've gone and lost my *pocket-book*. To-day is Saturday and the banks are all closed until Monday. I've got to have some money for the week-end. This is a very expensive coat, but I'm not asking much. I just want enough money to get me through the week-end. I'll come back Monday and *redeem* the coat!

The man waited, and said nothing. But when she pulled out the mink and allowed the beautiful thick fur

---

*pawnbroker,* one who lets you have money for an article of some val-ue which he then keeps until you pay the money back (with some money, called interest)

*pawn,* to leave (an article) with a pawnbroker

*stroke,* to touch gently with the hand

*pocket-book,* a small, flat case for holding bank notes and personal papers

*redeem,* to buy back (articles from a pawnbroker)

to fall over the counter his eyes opened up wide. He drew his hand away from the cat and came over to look at it. He picked it up and held it out in front of him.

'If only I had a watch on me or a ring,' Mrs Bixby said, 'I'd give you that instead. But the fact is I don't have a thing with me other than this coat.' She spread out her fingers for him to see.

'It looks new,' the man said and touched the soft fur gently.

'Oh, yes, it is. But as I said, I only want enough money to get me through till Monday. How about fifty dollars.'

'I'll *lend* you fifty dollars.'

'It's worth a hundred times more than that, but I know you'll take good care of it until I return.'

The man fetched a ticket and placed it on the counter. The ticket looked like one of those labels you tie on to your suitcase. But it had a line across the middle so that you could tear it in two.

'Name?' he asked.

'Leave that out. And the address.'

The man lifted the pen, waiting.

'You don't have to put the name and address, do you?'

The man shook his head and moved the pen on down to the next line.

'It's just that I'd rather not,' Mrs Bixby said. 'It's personal.'

'You'd better not lose this ticket, then.'

'I won't lose it.'

'Do you realize that anyone who gets hold of it can come in and claim the article?'

---

*lend,* to give the use of (something) for a time

'Yes, I know that.'

'What do you want me to put for a *description?*'

'No description either, thank you. It's not necessary. Just put the amount of money that you give me.'

The man waited again with the pen on the line beside the word ARTICLE.

'I think you ought to put a description. A description is always a help if you want to sell the ticket. You never know, you might want to sell it sometime.'

'I don't want to sell it.'

'You might have to. Lots of people do.'

'Look,' Mrs Bixby said. 'I'm not *broke,* if that's what you mean. I just want fifty dollars until Monday. Don't you understand?'

'You have it your own way then,' the man said. 'It's your coat.'

At this point an *unpleasant* thought struck Mrs Bixby. 'Tell me something,' she said. 'If I don't have a description on my ticket, how can I be sure you'll give me back the coat and not something else when I return?'

'It goes in the books.'

'But all I've got is a number. So you could hand me any old thing you wanted, isn't that so?'

'Do you want a description or don't you?' the man asked.

'No,' she said. 'I trust you.'

The man wrote »fifty dollars« opposite the word VALUE on both halves of the ticket. Then he tore off the

---

*description,* statement that describes
*broke,* completely without money
*unpleasant,* not pleasant

lower half and handed it to her. He took a *wallet* from the inside pocket of his jacket and produced five ten-dollar bills. 'The interest is three per cent a month,' he said.

'Yes, all right. And thank you. You'll take good care of it, won't you? Shall I put it in the box for you?'

'No,' the man said.

Mrs Bixby turned and went out of the shop on to the street where the taxi was waiting. Ten minutes later, she was home.

'Darling,' she said as she leaned forward and kissed her husband. 'Did you miss me?'

Cyril Bixby laid down the evening paper and looked at his watch. 'It's twelve and a half minutes past six,' he said. 'You're a bit late, aren't you?'

'I know. It's those trains. Aunt Maude sent you her love as usual. I'm dying for a drink, aren't you?'

The husband put away the newspaper and got up to get her a drink. His wife was watching him carefully, wondering how long she ought to wait. He had his back to her now as he was leaning forward to measure the gin. He was putting his face right up close to the measurer and staring into it as though it were a patient's mouth.

It was funny how small he always looked after the Colonel. I really must try to make him change the way he dresses, she told herself. His suits are just too *ridiculous*. There had been a time when she thought those Edwardian jackets were wonderful. Now they just seemed absurd. So did the narrow trousers. You had to have a special sort of face to wear things like that, and Cyril

---

*wallet,* pocket-book
*ridiculous,* very silly; to be laughed at

just didn't have it. He probably thought he was good-looking. He would like women to think that he was interested in them, that he was a bit of a dog. But Mrs Bixby knew better. There was nothing behind his manners. It meant nothing.

'Thank you, darling,' she said. She took the martini and seated herself. 'And what did you do last night?'

'I stayed on at the office and got the accounts up to date.'

'Now really, Cyril, I think it is high time you let other people do that kind of work for you. You're much too important for that sort of thing. Why doesn't that Pulteney woman do the accounts? That's part of her job, isn't it?'

'She does do them. But I have to price everything up first. She doesn't know who's rich and who isn't.'

'The martini is good,' Mrs Bixby said, setting down her glass on the side table. 'Very good.' She opened her bag and took out a tissue paper as if to blow her nose. 'Oh look!' she cried, seeing the ticket. 'I forgot to show you this! I found it just now on the seat of my taxi. It's got a number on it. I thought it might be a *lottery* ticket or something, so I kept it.'

She handed the small· piece of brown paper to her husband. He took it in his fingers and began looking at it closely as if it were a sick tooth.

'You know what this is?' he said slowly.

'No dear, I don't.'

'It's a pawn ticket.'

'A what?'

'A ticket from a pawnbroker. Here's the name and

---

*lottery*, a game in which people who have bought tickets can win money or articles

address of the shop, somewhere on Sixth Avenue.'

'Oh dear, I'm sorry. I was hoping it might be something more interesting.'

'There's no reason to be sorry,' Cyril Bixby said. 'As a matter of fact this could be rather *amusing.*'

'Why could it be amusing, darling?'

He explained to her carefully how a pawn ticket worked, and told her that anyone who had the ticket could claim the article.

'Do you think it's worth claiming?' she asked.

'I think it's worth finding out what it is. Do you see this figure of fifty dollars that's written here? Do you know what that means?'

'No, dear, what does it mean?'

'It means that the article in question is almost certain to be something of great value.'

'Do you mean it'll be worth fifty dollars?'

'More like five hundred.'

'Five hundred!'

'Don't you understand?' he said. 'A pawnbroker never gives you more than about a tenth of the real value.'

'Good lord! I never knew that.'

'There's a lot of things you don't know, my dear. Now listen to me. Since there's no name and address of the owner . . .'

'But there must be something to say who it belongs to?'

'Not a thing. People often do that. They don't want anyone to know they have been to a pawnbroker. They don't want anyone to think they are short of money.'

'Then you think we can keep it?'

---

*amusing,* that gives pleasure; funny

'Of course we can keep it. This is now o u r ticket.'

'You mean m y ticket,' Mrs Bixby said. 'I found it.'

'My dear girl, what does it matter? The important thing is that we can go and redeem it any time we like for only fifty dollars. How about that?'

'Oh, what fun!' she cried. 'And we don't even know what it is. It could be anything, isn't that right Cyril?'

'It could indeed, although it's probably either a ring or a watch. We shall just have to wait and see.'

'I think it's very interesting! Give me that ticket and I'll rush over first thing Monday and find out!'

'I think I had better do that.'

'Oh no!' she cried. 'Let m e do it!'

'I think not. I'll pick it up on my way to work.'

'But it's m y ticket! Please let me do it, Cyril! Why should you have all the fun?'

'You don't know these pawnbrokers, my dear. You may get *cheated.*'

'I wouldn't get cheated, I promise you I wouldn't. Give it to me, please.'

'Also you have to have fifty dollars,' he said smiling. 'You have to pay out fifty dollars before they'll give it to you.'

'I've got that,' she said. 'I think.'

'I would rather that you didn't go, if you don't mind.'

'But Cyril, I found it. It's mine. Whatever it is, it's mine, isn't that right?'

'Of course it's yours, my dear. There's no need to get so worked up about it.'

'I'm not. I'm just *excited,* that's all.'

---

*cheat,* here, to give back a wrong article
*excited,* not able to keep calm; not at rest

'I suppose you don't realize that this might be something for a man – a pocket-watch, for example. It isn't only women that go to pawnbrokers, you know.'

'In that case I'll give it to you for Christmas,' Mrs Bixby said. 'But if it's a woman's thing, I want it myself. Is that agreed?'

'That sounds very fair. Why don't you come with me? We could both go.'

Mrs Bixby was about to say yes to this, but caught herself just in time. She didn't want the pawnbroker to recognize her and thus let her husband get the idea that she had been there before.

'No,' she said slowly. 'I don't think I will. You see, it will be even more fun if I stay behind and wait. Oh, I do hope it isn't going to be something that neither of us wants.'

'You've got a point there,' he said. 'If I don't think it's worth fifty dollars, I won't even take it.'

'But you said it would be worth five hundred.'

'I'm quite sure it will. Don't worry.'

'Oh, Cyril, I can hardly wait! Isn't it *exciting*?'

'It's amusing,' he said, putting the ticket into his pocket. 'There's no doubt about that.'

Monday morning came at last. After breakfast Mrs Bixby followed her husband to the door and helped him on with his coat.

'Don't work too hard, darling,' she said.

'No, all right.'

'Home at six?'

'I hope so.'

---

*exciting*, that makes you excited

'Are you going to have time to go to that pawn-broker's?' she asked.

'My God, I forgot all about it. I'll take a taxi and go there now. It's on my way.'

'You haven't lost the ticket, have you?'

'I hope not,' he said, feeling in his pocket. 'No, here it is.'

'And you have enough money?'

'Just about.'

'Darling,' she said, 'if it happens to be something nice, something you think I might like, will you telephone me as soon as you get to the office?'

'If you want me to, yes.'

'You know, I hope it'll be something for you, Cyril. I'd much rather it was for you than for me.'

'That's very nice of you, my dear. Now I must run.'

About an hour later, when the telephone rang, Mrs Bixby ran so fast across the room that she reached it before the first ring had finished.

'I got it,' he said.

'You did! Oh, Cyril, what was it? Was it something good?'

'Good!' he cried. 'It's fantastic! You wait till you get your eyes on this!'

'Darling, what is it? Tell me quick!'

'You're a lucky girl, that's what you are.'

'It's for me, then?'

'Of course it's for you. Though how in the world it ever got pawned I just can't understand. Someone is crazy. You'll go mad when you see it.'

'What is it?'

'Try to guess.'

Mrs Bixby waited a moment. Be careful, she told herself. Be very careful now.

'A *diamond* ring?'

'Wrong. It's something you can wear.'

'Something I can wear? You mean like a hat?'

'No, it's not like a hat,' he said, laughing.

'Please, Cyril, tell me!'

'I want it to be a surprise. I'll bring it home with me this evening.'

'You'll do nothing of the sort!' she cried. 'I'm coming right down there to get it now!'

'I'd rather that you didn't do that.'

'Don't be so silly, darling. Why shouldn't I come?'

'Because I'm too busy. I'm half an hour behind already.'

'Then I'll come in the lunch hour. All right?'

'I'm not having a lunch hour. Oh, well, come at one thirty then, while I'm having a little to eat. Good-bye.'

At half past one, Mrs Bixby arrived at Mr Bixby's place of business and rang the bell. Her husband, in his white dentist's coat, opened the door himself.

'Oh, Cyril, I'm so excited.'

'You should be. You're a lucky girl, did you know that?' He let her into the *surgery*.

'Go and have your lunch, Miss Pulteney,' he said to the *assistant*, who was busy cleaning some instruments. 'You can finish that when you come back.' He waited until the girl had gone, then he walked over to the *cupboard* that he used for hanging up his clothes. He stood in front

---

*diamond,* a very expensive stone

*surgery,* here the room where the dentist works on a patient's teeth

*assistant,* here, a person who helps the dentist

*cupboard,* here a part of a room, set back from the rest, with a door, used for hanging clothes

of it and pointed at it with his finger. 'It's in there,' he said. 'Now – shut your eyes.'

Mrs Bixby did as she was told. In the silence that followed she could hear him open the cupboard door and pull out something from among the other things hanging there.

'All right! You can look!'

Mrs Bixby opened one eye just enough to see the man standing there in his white coat holding something up in the air.

'Mink!' he cried. 'Real mink!'

At the sound of that word she opened her eyes quick, and at the same time she started forward to take the coat in her arms.

But there was no coat. There was only a ridiculous little fur neckpiece hanging from her husband's hand.

'Look at that!' he said and waved it in front of her face.

Mrs Bixby put a hand up to her mouth and started backing away. I'm going to *scream,* she told herself. I just know it. I'm going to scream.

'What's the matter, my dear? Don't you like it?' He stopped waving the fur and stood staring at her, waiting for her to say something.

'Why yes,' she said. 'I . . . I . . . think it's . . . it's lovely . . . really lovely.'

'You really were surprised, weren't you?'

'Yes, I was.'

'Wonderful quality,' he said. 'Fine colour, too. You know something, my dear? I believe a piece like that would cost you two or three hundred dollars at least if you had to buy it in a shop.'

---

*scream,* to cry out in a loud voice

'I don't doubt it.'

There were two skins, two narrow skins with their heads still on, with glass eyes. One of them had the tail of the other in its mouth.

'Here,' he said. 'Try it on.' He put it around her neck and stepped back to admire it. 'Beautiful! It really suits you. It isn't everyone who has mink, my dear.'

'No, it isn't.'

'Better leave it behind when you go shopping or they will all think we're millionaires and charge us too much.'

'I'll try to remember that, Cyril.'

'I'm afraid you mustn't expect anything for Christmas. Fifty dollars was rather more than I was going to spend anyway.'

He began to wash his hands. 'Run along now, my dear, and buy yourself a nice lunch. I'd take you out myself but I've got a patient in the waiting-room.'

Mrs Bixby moved towards the door.

I'm going to kill that pawnbroker, she told herself. I'm going right back to the shop this very minute. I'm going to throw this ridiculous neckpiece right in his face and if he refuses to give me back my coat I'm going to kill him.

'Did I tell you I was going to be late home tonight?' Cyril Bixby said, still washing his hands.

'No.'

'It'll probably be at least eight thirty the way things look at the moment. It may even be nine.'

'Yes, all right. Good-bye.' Mrs Bixby went out and *slammed* the door behind her.

At that very moment, Miss Pulteney, the secretary-

---

*slam,* to shut with a loud noise

assistant, came sailing past her on her way to lunch.

'Isn't it a marvellous day?' Miss Pulteney said as she went by and smiled at her. She looked like a queen, just like a queen, in the beautiful black mink coat that the Colonel had given to Mrs Bixby.

# Questions

1. What is the writer's opinion of American women?

2. How does Mrs Bixby cover up her visits to the Colonel?

3. What are her feelings when the Colonel can't see her anymore?

4. Why can't she bring his parting gift home with her?

5. What does she tell the pawnbroker?

6. What is Mrs Bixby's opinion of her husband?

7. How does she explain the pawnbroker's ticket to him?

8. Why is it the husband, and not Mrs Bixby, who goes to redeem the ticket?

9. How does Mr Bixby surprise his wife?